Drips, Drops, and Saving ⌐

Management for Student

CW00734913

Carlos Silva

TABLE OF CONTENTS

Chapter 4: Water Conservation Strategies for Agriculture 22

Crop Selection and Water Requirements

Mulching: Reducing Evaporation and Soil Moisture Loss

Rainwater Harvesting: Capturing and Utilizing Precipitation

Soil Management: Improving Water Retention and Infiltration

Chapter 5: Water Saving Technologies and Innovations 30

Sensor-Based Irrigation Systems: Monitoring and Adjusting Water Usage

Smart Irrigation Controllers: Automating Watering Based on Weather Conditions

Crop Water Stress Index: Optimizing Irrigation Timing

Precision Agriculture: Integrating Technology for Efficient Water Management

Chapter 6: Community Involvement and Water Education 39

Promoting Water Conservation at School and Home

Participating in Community Water Conservation Initiatives

Educating Others on the Importance of Water Management

Chapter 7: Case Studies: Successful Water Management Projects 45

Sustainable Agriculture Practices in [Specific Region]

Water Conservation Efforts in [Specific School or Community]

Learning from Real-Life Examples: Lessons and Takeaways

Chapter 8: Overcoming Challenges in Water Management 52

Dealing with Water Scarcity and Drought Conditions

Addressing Water Pollution and Contamination

Balancing Water Needs with Environmental Concerns

Chapter 9: The Future of Water Management and Student Sustainability 58

Exploring Emerging Technologies and Innovations

Student-Led Initiatives and Projects for Water Conservation

Advocating for Sustainable Water Policies and Practices

Chapter 10: Conclusion and Call to Action 64

Reflecting on the Importance of Water Management

Empowering Students to Make a Difference

Taking Steps Towards a Sustainable Future

Chapter 1: Introduction to Water Management

Understanding the Importance of Water Conservation

Water is a finite resource that is vital for all life on Earth, including plants, animals, and humans. However, with the growing population and increasing demands for water, it is crucial for us to understand the importance of water conservation. In this subchapter, we will delve into the significance of conserving water and explore ways in which students can contribute to environmental sustainability.

Water conservation is the practice of using water wisely and efficiently to reduce unnecessary water usage. It plays a pivotal role in preserving the environment and ensuring a sustainable future. One of the key reasons for conserving water is to protect our ecosystems. Freshwater habitats, such as rivers, lakes, and wetlands, are home to numerous species of plants and animals. By conserving water, we can maintain the health and integrity of these habitats, supporting biodiversity and preserving delicate ecosystems.

Another critical reason for water conservation is the preservation of our natural resources. Freshwater is not an unlimited resource, and it takes a considerable amount of energy and resources to treat and deliver clean water to our homes and communities. By using water efficiently, we can reduce the strain on water treatment facilities and minimize the need for costly infrastructure development, such as new dams or reservoirs.

Water conservation also has a direct impact on our daily lives. By using water efficiently, we can save money on our utility bills. Simple changes, such as fixing leaky faucets or taking shorter showers, can significantly reduce water waste and lower our water bills. Additionally, conserving water helps to ensure a reliable water supply for future generations. As the global population continues to grow, it is essential to manage our water resources responsibly to avoid water scarcity and conflicts.

Students have a crucial role to play in water conservation and environmental sustainability. By adopting water-saving habits at home and in school, students can set an example and inspire others to do the same. Educating themselves and their peers about the importance of water conservation is vital. Simple actions, such as turning off the tap while brushing teeth, using water-efficient appliances, and collecting rainwater for gardening, can make a significant difference.

In conclusion, understanding the importance of water conservation is essential for students and the environment. By conserving water, we can protect ecosystems, preserve natural resources, save money, and ensure a reliable water supply for future generations. Students have the power to make a positive impact by adopting water-saving habits and spreading awareness about the significance of water conservation. Together, we can create a more sustainable and greener future.

Exploring the Relationship Between Water and Sustainability

Water is an essential resource that sustains life on our planet. It plays a crucial role in maintaining the balance of our ecosystems and supporting human activities. Understanding the relationship between water and sustainability is vital for students interested in the environment and its preservation.

Water is a precious resource that is finite in supply. It is crucial to manage water resources sustainably to ensure their availability for future generations. By exploring this relationship, we can learn how to conserve water and use it efficiently, ultimately contributing to the overall sustainability of our planet.

One aspect of water sustainability is the conservation of water resources. Students can learn about the importance of reducing water wastage in their daily lives. Simple actions such as turning off the tap while brushing teeth, fixing leaky faucets, or using water-efficient appliances can make a significant difference in water conservation efforts. By understanding the value of water and adopting sustainable practices, students can actively contribute to preserving this precious resource.

Water management is another critical aspect of water sustainability. Students can explore various methods of managing water resources effectively, such as rainwater harvesting, water recycling, and using technology to monitor water usage. Learning about these techniques can empower students to make informed decisions about water management and implement sustainable practices in their communities.

Furthermore, understanding the relationship between water and sustainability can shed light on the impact of human activities on water quality. Students can learn about the importance of protecting water bodies from pollution and the detrimental effects of contaminants on aquatic ecosystems. By exploring this relationship, students can become advocates for clean water and take actions to prevent pollution.

The exploration of the relationship between water and sustainability also extends to the global context. Students can learn about water scarcity and its impact on regions around the world. Understanding the challenges faced by communities without access to clean water can inspire students to take action and support initiatives aimed at providing clean water to those in need.

In conclusion, the relationship between water and sustainability is a crucial topic for students interested in the environment. By exploring this relationship, students can learn about water conservation, management, and the impact of human activities on water quality. This knowledge empowers students to become proactive in preserving water resources and working towards a sustainable future.

Chapter 2: The Water Cycle and Its Role in Agriculture

The Basics of the Water Cycle

Water is essential for life on Earth, and understanding the water cycle is crucial for students interested in the environment and sustainability. The water cycle, also known as the hydrological cycle, describes the continuous movement of water on, above, and below the Earth's surface. In this subchapter, we will explore the basics of the water cycle and its significance for our planet's well-being.

The water cycle consists of several interconnected processes: evaporation, condensation, precipitation, and runoff. Evaporation occurs when the sun's heat causes water from oceans, rivers, lakes, and even plants and animals to turn into water vapor or gas. This water vapor then rises into the atmosphere, forming clouds through a process called condensation.

Condensation happens when the water vapor cools down and turns back into liquid water droplets. These droplets accumulate and form clouds, which can be seen in the sky. When these water droplets become too heavy, they fall back to the Earth's surface as precipitation. Precipitation can take various forms, including rain, snow, sleet, or hail, depending on the temperature and atmospheric conditions.

Once precipitation reaches the Earth's surface, it can either be absorbed into the soil or collected in bodies of water. This stage of the water cycle is called runoff, and it plays a vital role in replenishing groundwater, rivers, and lakes. Runoff also helps transport nutrients and minerals from the land to aquatic ecosystems, supporting the growth of plants and sustaining the diverse organisms that depend on water.

Understanding the water cycle is crucial for environmental sustainability. By recognizing the importance of each stage, students can appreciate the delicate balance of our planet's water resources. Furthermore, knowledge of the water cycle allows us to make informed decisions about water management, conservation, and protection.

In conclusion, the water cycle is a fundamental process that sustains life on Earth. Through evaporation, condensation, precipitation, and runoff, water is continuously circulating, ensuring a constant supply of fresh water for all living organisms. By grasping the basics of the water cycle, students can actively contribute to environmental preservation and sustainable water management.

Water's Impact on Crop Growth and Development

In the world of agriculture, water plays a crucial role in the growth and development of crops. It is a vital resource that directly influences the quality and quantity of our food production. Understanding the impact of water on crop growth is essential for students interested in environmental sustainability and the future of food security.

Water availability is one of the most critical factors affecting crop development. Different crops have varying water requirements, and the availability of water directly affects their growth rate, nutrient uptake, and overall health. Insufficient water can lead to stunted growth, reduced yields, and even crop failure. On the other hand, excessive water can cause waterlogging, root suffocation, and disease outbreaks. Therefore, it is essential to strike the right balance and provide crops with just the right amount of water they need.

One of the key benefits of water in crop growth is its role in nutrient absorption. Water acts as a carrier, transporting essential nutrients from the soil to the plants' roots. Without adequate water, plants cannot take up nutrients effectively, leading to nutrient deficiencies and poor crop health. Additionally, water helps in the process of photosynthesis, where plants convert sunlight into energy. Without enough water, this vital process is hindered, affecting the overall growth and productivity of the crops.

Water management techniques also play a significant role in optimizing crop growth and reducing water wastage. Drip irrigation, for example, is an efficient method that delivers water directly to the plant roots, minimizing evaporation and runoff. This technique not only conserves water but also ensures that crops receive water precisely where they need it the most. Other water-saving techniques include mulching, which helps retain soil moisture, and rainwater harvesting, which collects and stores water for future use.

As students interested in the environment and sustainability, it is crucial to recognize the impact of water on crop growth. By understanding the water requirements of different crops and implementing efficient water management practices, we can contribute to sustainable agriculture and the preservation of our natural resources. Water scarcity is a growing concern worldwide, and it is our responsibility to ensure the responsible use and conservation of water in crop production.

In conclusion, water's impact on crop growth and development is undeniable. From nutrient absorption to photosynthesis, water plays a vital role in ensuring healthy and productive crops. By learning about water management techniques and implementing sustainable practices, students can contribute to the preservation of our environment and the future of food security. Let us embrace the importance of water in agriculture and work towards a more sustainable and water-efficient future.

Chapter 3: Water Management Techniques for Efficient Irrigation

Introduction to Efficient Irrigation Systems

Water is a precious resource, and managing it efficiently is crucial for the sustainability of our environment. In this subchapter, we will explore the concept of efficient irrigation systems and their importance in conserving water and ensuring the long-term viability of agricultural practices. This knowledge will empower students to make informed decisions and contribute to a more sustainable future.

Efficient irrigation systems are designed to deliver water precisely to plants in the most efficient and effective manner. Traditional irrigation methods such as flood irrigation or overhead sprinklers often result in significant water loss due to evaporation, runoff, and inefficient distribution. In contrast, efficient irrigation systems minimize these losses by delivering water directly to the root zone of plants, where it is needed most.

One popular and effective method of efficient irrigation is drip irrigation. Drip irrigation involves the use of a network of pipes or tubing with small holes or emitters placed near the plants' roots. This method delivers water slowly and directly to the plants, ensuring minimal waste. Drip irrigation not only reduces water consumption but also promotes healthier plant growth by preventing waterlogging and minimizing weed growth.

Another efficient irrigation system is known as micro-irrigation or sprinkler irrigation. This method uses low-pressure sprinklers or misters to distribute water evenly over a designated area. By delivering water in a fine mist, this system reduces water loss through evaporation and improves water penetration into the soil.

Efficient irrigation systems offer several benefits, not only in terms of water conservation but also in terms of energy savings and improved crop yields. By using water more efficiently, farmers can reduce their reliance on groundwater and surface water sources, which are often overexploited. Additionally, efficient irrigation systems can minimize the energy required to pump and transport water, reducing carbon emissions and environmental impact.

As students interested in the environment, it is essential to understand the significance of efficient irrigation systems. By implementing these systems in agricultural practices, we can contribute to the preservation of water resources and ensure the long-term sustainability of our ecosystems. Moreover, the adoption of efficient irrigation systems can inspire others to make environmentally conscious choices, leading to a more sustainable future for all.

In the next section, we will delve deeper into the different components and techniques used in efficient irrigation systems, providing students with practical knowledge to implement these systems in real-world scenarios.

Drip Irrigation: Maximizing Water Efficiency

In today's world, where concerns about the environment and sustainable living are growing, it is crucial for students to understand the importance of water management and conservation. One of the most effective methods of water efficiency in agriculture is through the use of drip irrigation. This subchapter aims to shed light on the principles and benefits of drip irrigation, addressing students who are interested in environmental issues and sustainable practices.

Drip irrigation is a system that delivers water directly to the roots of plants, utilizing a network of pipes, valves, and emitters. Unlike traditional irrigation methods, which often result in water wastage due to evaporation and runoff, drip irrigation ensures that water is delivered precisely where it is needed, minimizing water loss and maximizing efficiency.

There are several key advantages to using drip irrigation. Firstly, it reduces water usage significantly. By providing water directly to the plant's root zone, this method eliminates water loss from wind, runoff, or evaporation. As a result, plants receive the necessary moisture while minimizing water waste, making it an ideal choice for areas facing water scarcity or drought conditions.

Secondly, drip irrigation promotes plant health and growth. By delivering water directly to the roots, plants can absorb moisture more efficiently, leading to healthier and more productive crops. This method also helps to prevent diseases caused by excessive moisture on the leaves, as the foliage remains dry.

Additionally, drip irrigation contributes to soil conservation. Unlike some other irrigation methods that can lead to soil erosion, drip irrigation minimizes the risk of soil erosion by delivering water at a slow and steady pace. The water infiltrates into the soil gradually, allowing plants to absorb it effectively while decreasing the chance of runoff and soil degradation.

Lastly, drip irrigation is compatible with sustainable farming practices. It can be easily combined with organic farming methods, such as mulching and composting. By reducing the need for synthetic fertilizers and pesticides, drip irrigation supports environmentally friendly agricultural practices.

In conclusion, drip irrigation is a vital tool for maximizing water efficiency in agriculture, offering numerous benefits for both the environment and crop productivity. As students interested in environmental issues and sustainability, understanding and promoting the use of drip irrigation can contribute to the conservation and responsible management of our precious water resources.

Sprinkler Irrigation: Balancing Water Conservation and Crop Needs

In the realm of sustainable agriculture, finding the delicate balance between conserving water resources and meeting the crop's needs is of paramount importance. This challenge is where sprinkler irrigation systems play a vital role. Sprinkler irrigation is a technique that involves the distribution of water over the field in the form of small droplets, simulating rainfall. It is an effective method widely used in modern agriculture to ensure optimal crop growth while minimizing water wastage.

One of the significant advantages of sprinkler irrigation is its ability to conserve water. Unlike traditional flood irrigation, which often results in excessive water runoff and evaporation, sprinklers deliver water directly to the plant's root zone. This targeted approach reduces water loss and enhances overall water efficiency. By using sprinklers, farmers can precisely control the amount of water applied, adjusting it to match the specific needs of each crop. This not only saves water but also prevents over-irrigation, which can lead to waterlogging and nutrient leaching.

Another aspect that makes sprinkler irrigation an environmentally friendly choice is its compatibility with water-saving technologies. For instance, using weather-based sensors, farmers can automate their sprinkler systems to activate only when necessary, based on real-time weather conditions. This feature reduces unnecessary watering during periods of rainfall or high humidity, further conserving precious water resources. Additionally, incorporating soil moisture sensors can provide accurate data on the soil's water content, allowing farmers to apply water only when the crop truly requires it.

Furthermore, sprinkler irrigation promotes uniform water distribution throughout the field, ensuring that every plant receives adequate moisture. This even watering pattern helps prevent drought stress and fosters healthier plant growth. Additionally, the overhead spray of water can help cool the crop and reduce heat stress during hot summer days, contributing to a better overall yield.

However, it is crucial to acknowledge that sprinkler irrigation systems also come with certain limitations. They may not be suitable for all types of soil and terrain, as uneven surfaces can lead to water runoff or ponding in some areas. Furthermore, wind can affect the efficiency of sprinklers by causing water drift or uneven distribution. Therefore, proper planning, maintenance, and monitoring are essential to overcome these challenges and optimize the system's performance.

In conclusion, sprinkler irrigation offers a sustainable solution to balance water conservation and crop needs. By utilizing this efficient technique in agriculture, students and farmers can contribute to environmental preservation while ensuring healthy crop growth. Understanding the principles and challenges associated with sprinkler irrigation can empower future generations to make informed decisions and embrace sustainable water management practices for a greener and more food-secure future.

Flood Irrigation: Traditional Methods and Modern Modifications

Water is a precious resource, and managing it efficiently is crucial for sustainable agriculture. One of the oldest and most traditional methods of irrigation is flood irrigation, which has been practiced for centuries. In this subchapter, we will explore the traditional methods of flood irrigation and the modern modifications that have been introduced to improve its efficiency and reduce water wastage.

Traditionally, flood irrigation involves diverting water from a nearby source, such as a river or canal, and allowing it to flow freely over the fields. This method is simple and cost-effective, making it popular among farmers worldwide. However, it has several drawbacks, including uneven water distribution, excessive runoff, and the potential for waterlogging and soil erosion.

To address these issues, modern modifications have been developed to enhance the efficiency of flood irrigation. One such modification is the use of levees and furrows. Levees are small embankments constructed around the fields to contain the water within designated areas, while furrows are shallow trenches that allow the water to flow evenly across the field. This ensures a more uniform distribution of water, minimizing water wastage and reducing the risk of soil erosion.

Another modification is the implementation of precision grading. Precision grading involves leveling the field to eliminate high and low spots, ensuring that water spreads evenly across the entire area. This technique helps prevent waterlogging in certain areas and promotes better water infiltration into the soil.

Furthermore, the use of modern technology has significantly improved flood irrigation practices. Automated systems, such as timers and sensors, can be installed to control the release of water, ensuring it is delivered at the right time and in the right amount. This not only saves water but also optimizes crop growth by providing the required moisture at the appropriate stages of growth.

In conclusion, flood irrigation has been a traditional method of water management in agriculture. However, to make it more sustainable and efficient, modern modifications have been introduced. These modifications, including the use of levees and furrows, precision grading, and automated systems, help improve water distribution, reduce water wastage, and promote better crop growth. By understanding and implementing these modifications, students can play a vital role in conserving water resources and ensuring a sustainable future for our environment.

Chapter 4: Water Conservation Strategies for Agriculture

Crop Selection and Water Requirements

In the pursuit of sustainable agriculture and responsible environmental stewardship, it is crucial for students to understand the significance of crop selection and its water requirements. In this subchapter, we will delve into the various factors that influence crop selection and discuss the importance of water management in sustainable farming practices.

When it comes to choosing crops, several factors must be taken into consideration, such as climate, soil type, market demand, and available water resources. Different crops have varying water requirements, and selecting the appropriate ones can significantly impact water conservation efforts.

Firstly, understanding the local climate is vital in determining suitable crops for a specific region. Some crops thrive in arid conditions, while others require more water to flourish. By choosing crops that are well-adapted to the local climate, students can minimize water usage and optimize yields.

Moreover, soil type plays a crucial role in crop selection. Certain crops perform better in sandy soils, while others prefer loamy or clayey soils. Soil characteristics affect water retention and drainage, which directly impact irrigation needs. Opting for crops that are compatible with the prevalent soil type can enhance water efficiency and reduce the risk of waterlogging or drought stress.

Market demand is another aspect to consider when selecting crops. Students should research and identify crops that have high market value and demand in their region. By growing crops with a strong market demand, students can promote local economic sustainability while ensuring efficient water usage.

However, the most critical factor in crop selection for environmental sustainability is water requirements. Students must prioritize crops that have low water requirements, as this will reduce the strain on local water resources. Drought-tolerant crops, such as millets, sorghum, or certain varieties of beans, can be excellent options for regions with limited water availability. Additionally, incorporating efficient irrigation methods like drip irrigation or rainwater harvesting can further minimize water usage and maximize crop productivity.

In conclusion, crop selection and water requirements are integral components of sustainable agriculture and environmental preservation. By considering factors such as climate, soil type, market demand, and water requirements, students can make informed choices that promote water conservation and long-term sustainability. Selecting crops with low water requirements, coupled with efficient irrigation techniques, will not only benefit the environment but also ensure the economic viability and resilience of farming practices. Let us strive to make wise choices in crop selection and water management to secure a greener and more sustainable future.

Mulching: Reducing Evaporation and Soil Moisture Loss

In our quest for sustainable practices, understanding the importance of water conservation is crucial. One effective method that can significantly contribute to water management is mulching. Mulching is the process of covering the soil surface with a layer of organic or inorganic materials, such as wood chips, straw, leaves, or plastic. This subchapter will delve into the benefits of mulching in reducing evaporation and soil moisture loss, highlighting its significance for environmental preservation.

Evaporation is a natural process where water turns into vapor and escapes into the atmosphere. However, excessive evaporation can lead to a decrease in soil moisture, affecting plant growth and the overall ecosystem. Mulching acts as a barrier, preventing direct contact between the soil and the atmosphere, thus reducing evaporation. By covering the soil with an organic layer, mulching retains moisture, keeping the soil cool and damp for longer periods. This is particularly important during hot and dry seasons when water scarcity is a pressing concern.

Mulching also aids in reducing soil moisture loss, which is crucial for maintaining a healthy balance in the environment. When water availability is limited, plants struggle to survive, and the delicate ecological balance is disturbed. By conserving soil moisture, mulching ensures that plants have a continuous supply of water, promoting their growth and enabling them to withstand drought conditions. Additionally, mulching enhances soil structure by preventing erosion and compaction, which further aids in moisture retention.

For students passionate about environmental preservation, understanding the impact of mulching on water management is essential. By implementing mulching practices in gardens, parks, and agricultural fields, students can actively contribute to sustainable water management. Mulching not only conserves water but also reduces the need for frequent irrigation, saving both time and resources. Moreover, the organic materials used in mulching decompose over time, enriching the soil with nutrients, fostering a healthy ecosystem, and reducing the dependency on chemical fertilizers.

In conclusion, mulching plays a vital role in reducing evaporation and soil moisture loss. Its significance for the environment cannot be overstated, especially in the face of climate change and water scarcity challenges. By incorporating mulching practices into their daily lives, students can actively contribute to the preservation of our natural resources and promote a sustainable future.

Rainwater Harvesting: Capturing and Utilizing Precipitation

Rainwater harvesting is a sustainable and environmentally friendly practice that involves capturing and utilizing precipitation for various purposes. In this subchapter, we will explore the benefits, techniques, and applications of rainwater harvesting, with a focus on how students can contribute to water management and environmental sustainability.

1.   The   Importance   of   Rainwater   Harvesting: With increasing water scarcity and the environmental impact of traditional water sources, rainwater harvesting has emerged as a vital solution. By capturing rainwater, we can reduce strain on local water supplies, conserve energy, and minimize runoff, which can lead to soil erosion and pollution of natural water bodies.

2.   Techniques   for   Rainwater   Harvesting: There are several techniques for harvesting rainwater, ranging from simple to advanced systems. Basic rain barrels or cisterns can be used to collect rainwater from rooftops, which can then be used for watering plants, washing vehicles, or even flushing toilets. More complex systems involve the use of underground tanks and filtration mechanisms to store and purify rainwater for drinking purposes.

3.   Applications   of   Rainwater   Harvesting: Rainwater harvesting has a wide range of applications that can benefit both individuals and communities. In homes and schools, harvested rainwater can be used for irrigation, reducing the need for expensive and energy-intensive municipal water supplies. It can also be treated

and used as a source of drinking water, particularly in areas where clean water is scarce or unreliable.

4.   Students'   Role   in   Rainwater   Harvesting:
As students, you play a crucial role in promoting rainwater harvesting and water management for sustainability. You can raise awareness about the benefits of rainwater harvesting among your peers, teachers, and community members. Consider organizing workshops or events to educate others about the techniques and importance of rainwater harvesting.

Moreover, you can actively participate in rainwater harvesting projects in your school or local community. This could involve installing rain barrels, designing and implementing larger-scale harvesting systems, or advocating for policy changes that support rainwater harvesting initiatives.

By actively engaging in rainwater harvesting, you can contribute to the preservation of water resources, reduce your ecological footprint, and inspire others to adopt sustainable practices.

In conclusion, rainwater harvesting offers a practical and effective solution to address water scarcity and environmental concerns. By capturing and utilizing precipitation, students can play an active role in water management and contribute to a more sustainable future. Embrace the power of rainwater harvesting and become an advocate for responsible water usage.

Soil Management: Improving Water Retention and Infiltration

Water is a vital resource for sustaining life on our planet, and its efficient management is crucial for a sustainable future. In the realm of agriculture and environmental conservation, soil management plays a pivotal role in improving water retention and infiltration. By understanding and implementing proper soil management techniques, we can ensure a more efficient use of water resources while promoting a healthy environment.

Water retention refers to the ability of soil to hold onto moisture instead of allowing it to drain away. Adequate water retention is essential for plant growth, as it ensures a steady supply of water to the roots. One of the key factors affecting water retention is soil structure. Healthy soils with good structure, rich in organic matter, have a greater capacity to retain water. As students interested in environmental sustainability, understanding the importance of soil structure and organic matter is crucial. By adopting practices like composting, cover cropping, and reducing chemical inputs, we can enhance soil structure and improve water retention.

Infiltration, on the other hand, refers to the process by which water enters the soil. Efficient infiltration is vital for preventing water runoff and erosion. Compacted soils, often found in urban areas or intensively managed agricultural fields, have low infiltration rates, leading to increased runoff and subsequent water pollution. Implementing soil management techniques such as mulching, using terraces or contour plowing, and avoiding over-tilling can significantly improve infiltration rates. As students concerned about the environment, we can advocate for the adoption of these techniques to reduce water pollution and protect our natural ecosystems.

In addition to soil structure and management practices, vegetation cover also plays a critical role in improving water retention and infiltration. Plant roots create channels within the soil, allowing water to penetrate deeper. By promoting the growth of vegetation, such as grasses, shrubs, and trees, we can enhance water infiltration and reduce the risk of soil erosion. As students passionate about the environment, we can actively participate in tree-planting initiatives, establish community gardens, or advocate for the preservation of natural habitats.

In conclusion, soil management techniques are paramount in improving water retention and infiltration, which are essential for sustainable water management. By understanding the significance of soil structure, organic matter, and vegetation cover, students can actively contribute to environmental preservation. By implementing these practices in our daily lives and advocating for their adoption on a larger scale, we can make a significant impact in conserving water resources and promoting a sustainable future for generations to come.

Chapter 5: Water Saving Technologies and Innovations

Sensor-Based Irrigation Systems: Monitoring and Adjusting Water Usage

In recent years, the world has witnessed an alarming increase in water scarcity issues. As students and individuals concerned about the environment, it is crucial for us to explore innovative solutions to conserve this precious resource. One such solution is the development of sensor-based irrigation systems, which play a vital role in monitoring and adjusting water usage for agricultural purposes. This subchapter will delve into the various aspects of sensor-based irrigation systems and their significance in promoting sustainable water management practices.

Sensor-based irrigation systems utilize advanced technology to monitor soil moisture levels, weather conditions, and plant water requirements. These sensors provide real-time data, enabling farmers to make informed decisions about when and how much water to apply to their crops. By continuously monitoring the soil moisture content, these systems prevent over-irrigation, which can lead to water waste, nutrient leaching, and damage to plant health. Additionally, they allow for precise irrigation scheduling, reducing the risk of under-watering and ensuring optimal crop growth.

Not only do sensor-based irrigation systems conserve water, but they also enhance crop yield and quality. By providing plants with the right amount of water at the right time, these systems promote efficient nutrient absorption and root development. This, in turn, leads to healthier and more resilient crops, reducing the need for excessive pesticide or fertilizer application. Moreover, these systems can detect early signs of plant stress, such as water deficiency or disease, allowing farmers to take timely action and prevent yield losses.

Sensor-based irrigation systems are not only beneficial for farmers but also for the environment as a whole. By minimizing water usage, these systems contribute to the preservation of freshwater resources, which are becoming increasingly scarce. Moreover, they reduce the energy consumption associated with pumping and distributing water, helping to lower greenhouse gas emissions. Ultimately, the adoption of sensor-based irrigation systems promotes sustainable farming practices and contributes to the overall goal of achieving a greener and more environmentally friendly agricultural sector.

As students, we have a crucial role to play in advocating for the implementation of sensor-based irrigation systems. By raising awareness about these innovative technologies, we can encourage farmers and agricultural organizations to embrace them as part of their water management strategies. Additionally, we can support research and development initiatives that aim to improve the efficiency and affordability of these systems, making them accessible to farmers of all scales and regions.

In conclusion, sensor-based irrigation systems are revolutionizing the way water is used in agriculture. By monitoring soil moisture levels and adjusting water usage accordingly, these systems not only conserve water but also enhance crop productivity and reduce environmental impact. As students passionate about the environment, we must champion the adoption of these systems and promote sustainable water management practices for a greener and more sustainable future.

Smart Irrigation Controllers: Automating Watering Based on Weather Conditions

In the quest for a sustainable future, it is imperative that we address one of the most critical issues facing our planet today - water management. As students, we have the power to make a difference by embracing innovative solutions that promote environmental conservation. This chapter focuses on an exciting technology that holds immense potential in water management: smart irrigation controllers.

Traditional irrigation systems often rely on fixed schedules, resulting in excessive water usage and inefficient distribution. Smart irrigation controllers revolutionize this process by automating watering based on real-time weather conditions. By integrating weather data, these controllers can adjust watering schedules, duration, and frequency to match the specific needs of plants and landscapes.

One of the key advantages of smart irrigation controllers is their ability to optimize water usage. By considering factors such as rainfall, humidity, wind speed, and temperature, these controllers ensure that plants receive just the right amount of water, reducing waste and conserving this precious resource. Not only does this benefit the environment, but it also helps students save on water bills, making it a win-win situation.

Furthermore, smart irrigation controllers offer convenience and ease of use. With the help of intuitive interfaces and smartphone applications, students can monitor and control their irrigation system from anywhere at any time. This empowers them to manage their landscapes efficiently, even when they are away from home or busy with other commitments.

In addition to water conservation, smart irrigation controllers contribute to the overall health and vitality of plants. By providing the correct amount of water at the right time, they prevent overwatering and subsequent issues such as root rot and fungal diseases. This not only promotes plant growth but also reduces the need for chemical pesticides, aligning with the environmental niche and fostering a sustainable approach to gardening and landscaping.

As students, we have a responsibility to protect and preserve our environment. By adopting smart irrigation controllers, we can actively contribute to water conservation efforts while enhancing the overall sustainability of our communities. These controllers are not just technology, but tools that empower us to make a positive impact on our environment, reducing our carbon footprint, and ensuring a greener future for generations to come.

In conclusion, smart irrigation controllers represent a significant step forward in water management and sustainability. By automating watering based on weather conditions, these controllers optimize water usage, enhance plant health, and provide convenience for students. Embracing this technology is not only beneficial for our environment but also helps us develop a deeper understanding of the importance of responsible resource management. Together, let's make a difference and create a more sustainable world.

Crop Water Stress Index: Optimizing Irrigation Timing

In the realm of sustainable agriculture, optimizing irrigation practices is essential to ensure efficient water usage and maximize crop productivity. One valuable tool used by farmers and researchers alike is the Crop Water Stress Index (CWSI), which aids in determining the appropriate timing and amount of irrigation required for crops. This subchapter delves into the significance of CWSI and its role in enhancing environmental sustainability.

The CWSI is a metric that quantifies the water stress experienced by crops at a given time. It measures the balance between the water supply available to plants and their water requirements. By monitoring this index, farmers can make informed decisions about irrigation, preventing both overwatering and underwatering, which can have detrimental effects on crops and the environment.

Optimizing irrigation timing through the use of CWSI offers several benefits. Firstly, it helps conserve water resources by avoiding unnecessary irrigation. Overwatering not only wastes water but also leads to leaching of nutrients from the soil, contributing to pollution in nearby water bodies. By accurately assessing the water stress levels of crops, farmers can apply irrigation only when necessary, reducing water consumption and protecting the environment.

Secondly, optimizing irrigation timing aids in enhancing crop health and yield. Underwatering can lead to stunted growth, reduced yield, and even crop failure. By closely monitoring the CWSI, farmers can identify periods of high water stress and provide timely irrigation, ensuring that crops receive adequate water for optimal growth and productivity.

Furthermore, implementing CWSI-based irrigation strategies can contribute to climate change mitigation. Water scarcity is a pressing concern in many regions, and agriculture is a major consumer of water resources. By utilizing CWSI to optimize irrigation, farmers can reduce their water footprint, contributing to the overall conservation of water resources. This, in turn, helps mitigate the impacts of climate change by reducing the strain on freshwater ecosystems and minimizing greenhouse gas emissions associated with water extraction and distribution.

In conclusion, understanding and utilizing the Crop Water Stress Index can play a crucial role in optimizing irrigation practices and promoting environmental sustainability in agriculture. By closely monitoring the water stress levels of crops and adjusting irrigation accordingly, farmers can conserve water resources, enhance crop health and yield, and contribute to climate change mitigation. Incorporating the concept of CWSI into sustainable farming practices is an important step towards ensuring a greener and more sustainable future.

Precision Agriculture: Integrating Technology for Efficient Water Management

In an era where natural resources are becoming increasingly scarce, it is crucial for us, as students and environmental enthusiasts, to explore innovative ways to conserve water and promote sustainable practices in agriculture. One such technique that has gained significant attention is precision agriculture, which harnesses the power of technology to revolutionize water management in farming.

Precision agriculture, also known as smart farming, is an advanced approach that utilizes various technologies such as Geographic Information Systems (GIS), Global Positioning Systems (GPS), and remote sensing to optimize water usage in agricultural practices. By integrating these technologies, farmers can make informed decisions about irrigation, fertilization, and pest control, leading to not only enhanced crop quality and yield but also reduced water wastage.

The use of GIS and GPS enables farmers to precisely map their fields, providing accurate information about soil moisture levels, topography, and crop growth patterns. This information can then be used to create customized irrigation plans, ensuring that water is applied only where and when it is needed. By avoiding over-irrigation, farmers can prevent water runoff and leaching, reducing the risk of soil erosion and minimizing the contamination of water bodies with agricultural chemicals.

Remote sensing, another crucial component of precision agriculture, involves the use of satellites and drones equipped with specialized sensors to collect data on crop health and water stress. This data is then analyzed to detect any anomalies or signs of water deficiency, allowing farmers to take timely actions to rectify the issue. By identifying areas of the field that require additional water, farmers can avoid wasteful blanket irrigation and apply water only to the specific areas in need, resulting in significant water savings.

Furthermore, precision agriculture techniques also aid in the efficient use of fertilizers and pesticides, as they allow farmers to target specific areas that require treatment, reducing the overall amount of chemicals used. This not only minimizes the environmental impact but also saves water, as excess chemicals can leach into groundwater and contaminate water sources.

By embracing precision agriculture, we can pave the way for a more sustainable future, where water resources are conserved, and environmental impacts are minimized. As students, it is our responsibility to stay informed about these technological advancements and advocate for their implementation on a broader scale. By doing so, we can contribute to the preservation of our environment, ensuring a prosperous future for generations to come.

Chapter 6: Community Involvement and Water Education

Promoting Water Conservation at School and Home

Water is a precious resource that sustains life on Earth. As students who care about the environment, it is our responsibility to promote water conservation both at school and at home. By adopting simple yet effective water-saving practices, we can make a significant impact on preserving this vital resource for future generations.

At school, there are numerous ways we can promote water conservation. Firstly, we can encourage our fellow students and teachers to be mindful of their water usage. By reminding them to turn off the taps tightly after use and report any leakages promptly, we can prevent unnecessary water wastage. Additionally, we can organize awareness campaigns and workshops to educate our peers about the importance of water conservation and offer practical tips on how to reduce water consumption in their daily lives.

Another effective way to conserve water at school is by implementing water-saving technologies. Installing low-flow faucets and toilets in restrooms, as well as water-efficient irrigation systems for school gardens, can significantly reduce water usage. We can also advocate for rainwater harvesting systems to collect and reuse rainwater for non-potable purposes like watering plants and flushing toilets.

Water conservation should not be limited to the school environment alone. We must extend our efforts to our homes as well. Encouraging our family members to adopt water-saving practices can lead to significant water conservation at the household level. Simple actions such as taking shorter showers, fixing leaky faucets, and using dishwashers and washing machines only when they are fully loaded can contribute to saving thousands of gallons of water annually.

Furthermore, we can actively participate in community initiatives and engage with local environmental organizations that focus on water conservation. By joining forces with like-minded individuals, we can create a stronger voice for change and work towards implementing water-saving policies and practices in our neighborhoods.

Remember, every small step counts. By promoting water conservation at school and home, we can collectively make a significant impact on our environment. Let's be the responsible stewards of this precious resource and inspire others to join us in safeguarding our planet's most vital asset – water. Together, we can ensure a sustainable future for ourselves and generations to come.

Participating in Community Water Conservation Initiatives

Water is a finite resource, essential for all forms of life on Earth. It is our responsibility as individuals and communities to ensure its sustainable use. Participating in community water conservation initiatives is a powerful way for students to contribute to environmental preservation and create a positive impact on their surroundings. This subchapter explores various ways students can get involved in conserving water and promoting sustainability in their communities.

One of the most effective ways to conserve water is by raising awareness and educating others about its importance. Students can organize workshops, seminars, or awareness campaigns in their schools or local communities. By sharing knowledge about water conservation techniques, such as fixing leaky faucets, using water-efficient appliances, or practicing shorter showers, students can empower others to make conscious choices in their water usage.

Another way to contribute to community water conservation initiatives is by actively participating in local conservation projects. This could involve volunteering at local water treatment plants, joining community organizations dedicated to water conservation, or assisting in the creation of rainwater harvesting systems. By engaging in hands-on activities, students can gain practical experience and develop a deeper understanding of the challenges and solutions related to water management.

Furthermore, students can advocate for policy changes that promote sustainable water practices in their communities. This may involve writing letters to local government representatives, participating in public hearings, or even initiating petitions to implement water-saving measures in schools and public spaces. By actively engaging in the decision-making process, students can shape policies and regulations that prioritize the long-term availability of clean water.

Lastly, students can lead by example and encourage their peers, friends, and family members to adopt water-saving habits. By demonstrating the benefits of conserving water through personal actions, such as collecting rainwater or using reusable water bottles, students can inspire others to follow suit. Small changes in daily routines can have a significant impact when multiplied across a community.

In conclusion, participating in community water conservation initiatives allows students to actively contribute to the preservation of the environment. By raising awareness, participating in local projects, advocating for policy changes, and leading by example, students can play a crucial role in ensuring the sustainable use of water resources. Together, we can make a difference and create a more water-conscious and environmentally friendly society.

Educating Others on the Importance of Water Management

Water is a precious resource that sustains all life on Earth. It is essential for our survival, as well as for the health of our environment. However, water scarcity and pollution have become significant challenges in today's world. As students and members of the environment niche, it is our responsibility to educate others about the importance of water management and work towards sustainable practices.

In this subchapter, we will delve into the various aspects of water management and highlight its significance. We will explore the consequences of water misuse and the ways in which we can contribute to a more sustainable future.

To begin with, water management involves the responsible use, conservation, and protection of water resources. It includes practices such as reducing water waste, promoting efficient irrigation techniques, and preventing water pollution. By implementing these measures, we can ensure that water remains available for future generations and that ecosystems dependent on water thrive.

Water scarcity is a pressing issue globally, affecting both developed and developing nations. It is crucial to educate others about the consequences of water scarcity, which include food insecurity, health risks, and conflicts over limited water resources. By raising awareness about these issues, we can encourage individuals to adopt water-saving habits, such as turning off taps when not in use, repairing leaky faucets, and using water-efficient appliances.

Moreover, water pollution poses a significant threat to our environment. Contaminated water can harm aquatic life, damage ecosystems, and even lead to human health problems. Educating others about the sources of water pollution, such as industrial waste, agricultural runoff, and improper disposal of chemicals, can help prevent further degradation of water quality. We can also emphasize the importance of proper wastewater treatment and the use of eco-friendly products to minimize pollution.

As students, we have the power to create change. By organizing workshops, awareness campaigns, and community outreach programs, we can educate our peers and wider audiences about the importance of water management. We can also collaborate with local authorities and environmental organizations to advocate for sustainable water policies and regulations.

In conclusion, educating others about the significance of water management is crucial for our sustainable future. By raising awareness about water scarcity, pollution, and the ways in which we can contribute to conservation, we can inspire positive change within our communities. Let us take action and become ambassadors for water management, ensuring that future generations can enjoy the benefits of this vital resource.

Chapter 7: Case Studies: Successful Water Management Projects

Sustainable Agriculture Practices in [Specific Region]

In the quest for a greener and more sustainable future, the importance of sustainable agriculture practices cannot be overstated. [Specific Region], known for its rich natural resources and diverse agricultural sector, has made significant strides in adopting environmentally-friendly techniques to ensure the long-term viability of its farming practices.

One of the key principles of sustainable agriculture is soil conservation. In [Specific Region], farmers have recognized the importance of maintaining healthy soil by minimizing erosion and enhancing its fertility. Through practices such as contour plowing, terracing, and cover cropping, the region's farmers have successfully reduced soil erosion, retained moisture, and improved soil structure. By implementing these practices, they not only protect the environment but also improve crop yields, leading to increased profitability.

Another crucial aspect of sustainable agriculture in [Specific Region] is water management. Given the increasing scarcity of water resources, efficient irrigation techniques have become essential. Drip irrigation systems, for instance, deliver water directly to the plant's root zone, minimizing wastage and maximizing water use efficiency. This method not only conserves water but also reduces the risk of disease and weed growth. Through the installation of drip irrigation systems, farmers in [Specific Region] have experienced improved crop quality and higher yields while reducing their water consumption.

Integrated pest management (IPM) is yet another sustainable agriculture practice that has gained popularity in [Specific Region]. By combining biological, cultural, and chemical control methods, farmers can effectively manage pests while minimizing the use of harmful chemical pesticides. This approach promotes biodiversity, as it encourages the presence of natural predators and reduces the risk of pest resistance. Students interested in sustainable agriculture in [Specific Region] can learn about the various IPM techniques employed by local farmers, such as crop rotation, companion planting, and the use of pheromone traps.

Furthermore, [Specific Region] has embraced organic farming practices, which emphasize the use of natural fertilizers and pesticides. Organic farming eliminates the use of synthetic chemicals, reducing environmental pollution and promoting healthier soil and water resources. Students keen on sustainable agriculture can explore the local organic farming certification programs and gain insights into the challenges and benefits associated with organic farming practices in [Specific Region].

In conclusion, [Specific Region] has emerged as a leader in sustainable agriculture practices, showcasing the region's commitment to environmental conservation and long-term agricultural sustainability. By adopting soil conservation methods, efficient water management techniques, integrated pest management, and organic farming practices, the region's farmers are not only safeguarding the environment but also ensuring the future of their agricultural endeavors. Students interested in the environment and sustainable agriculture can draw inspiration from the sustainable practices employed in [Specific Region] and contribute to the global movement towards a more sustainable and resilient future.

Water Conservation Efforts in [Specific School or Community]

Water is a precious resource that sustains life on our planet. As responsible citizens, it is our duty to conserve water and ensure its availability for future generations. In [Specific School or Community], we have taken up the challenge to implement various water conservation efforts, making a positive impact on our environment.

One of the key initiatives in our school/community is the installation of water-efficient fixtures and appliances. We have replaced traditional faucets and toilets with low-flow models, reducing water consumption significantly. These changes not only save water but also contribute to lowering our utility bills, leaving more resources for other important activities.

Another important aspect of our water conservation efforts is education and awareness. We organize workshops, seminars, and awareness campaigns to educate students about the importance of water conservation. By involving students in hands-on activities, such as leak detection and water usage monitoring, we instill a sense of responsibility towards our environment. We also encourage students to share their knowledge with their families, friends, and the wider community, creating a ripple effect of positive change.

Our school/community has also implemented rainwater harvesting systems. These systems collect rainwater from rooftops, which is then stored and used for non-potable purposes such as watering plants and cleaning. By utilizing rainwater, we reduce our dependency on freshwater sources and alleviate the strain on our municipal water supply.

Additionally, we have established a water recycling program. Through this initiative, we treat and reuse water from various sources, such as greywater from sinks and showers. This recycled water is then used for irrigation purposes in our school/community gardens. By implementing such a program, we not only conserve water but also minimize the amount of wastewater being discharged into the environment.

To further encourage water conservation, we have implemented a reward system. Students who actively participate in water conservation efforts and demonstrate good water usage habits are recognized and rewarded. This helps to create a culture of conservation and motivates others to follow suit.

In conclusion, [Specific School or Community] is committed to water conservation efforts. Through the installation of water-efficient fixtures, education and awareness programs, rainwater harvesting, water recycling, and a reward system, we are making a significant contribution towards the sustainability of our environment. By conserving water today, we are ensuring a better tomorrow for ourselves and future generations. Let us all join hands and make water conservation a way of life.

Learning from Real-Life Examples: Lessons and Takeaways

In the journey towards achieving sustainability, one of the most valuable resources we have is real-life examples. By studying the experiences and lessons learned from environmental initiatives around the world, we can gain insights and inspiration for our own efforts. In this subchapter, we will explore some remarkable stories and their takeaways, all aimed at empowering students to become champions of water management and environmental conservation.

One such example comes from the city of Cape Town, South Africa, which faced a severe water crisis in recent years. In response, the city implemented strict water restrictions and launched a powerful public awareness campaign. The lessons learned from this crisis highlight the importance of proactive water management, conservation, and the need for a collective effort. Students can take inspiration from Cape Town's experience and become advocates for responsible water usage in their own communities.

Another compelling case study is the restoration of the Jordan River in the Middle East. This once-polluted river has been transformed into a symbol of hope and cooperation through the efforts of various organizations and communities. By studying this success story, students can learn about the significance of collaboration, the power of grassroots movements, and the positive impact of environmental restoration.

The lessons we can draw from these examples are not limited to large-scale initiatives. Even small-scale efforts at the individual level can make a significant difference. For instance, the story of a student-led rainwater harvesting project in a rural village showcases the potential of simple solutions. By installing rain barrels and educating the community about the importance of water conservation, these students were able to provide a sustainable water source and improve their quality of life.

Additionally, we will explore real-life examples of innovative technologies and practices that promote sustainable water management. From smart irrigation systems to green roofs and wastewater treatment plants, there are countless inspiring ideas that students can learn from and apply in their own lives.

By learning from real-life examples and understanding the lessons and takeaways they offer, students can become agents of change in the environmental niche. Through their actions, they can contribute to water conservation, promote sustainability, and inspire others to do the same. The stories shared in this subchapter will serve as a source of motivation and guidance, empowering students to make a positive impact on the environment and create a more sustainable future.

Chapter 8: Overcoming Challenges in Water Management

Dealing with Water Scarcity and Drought Conditions

Water scarcity and drought conditions pose significant challenges to both the environment and human societies. As students concerned about the environment, it is crucial for us to understand these issues and explore sustainable solutions. In this subchapter, we will delve into the causes and impacts of water scarcity and drought, as well as strategies to mitigate and adapt to these conditions.

Water scarcity occurs when the demand for water exceeds its availability in a particular region. It can be caused by various factors such as population growth, climate change, industrialization, and poor water management practices. Drought, on the other hand, refers to an extended period of abnormally low precipitation leading to water shortage in an area. Both water scarcity and drought have far-reaching consequences that can impact ecosystems, agriculture, and human well-being.

The environmental impacts of water scarcity and drought are severe. Aquatic habitats suffer as water bodies shrink or dry up, leading to the loss of biodiversity. Wetlands and forests, which depend on adequate water supply, are also negatively affected. In addition, drought conditions increase the risk of wildfires, further damaging ecosystems and releasing harmful greenhouse gases into the atmosphere.

Agriculture, a significant consumer of water, is significantly impacted by water scarcity and drought. Crops fail, livestock suffer, and food production becomes increasingly challenging. This, in turn, can lead to food shortages and higher prices, affecting communities and economies.

To address these challenges, sustainable water management practices are crucial. Conservation and efficient use of water resources play a vital role in combating water scarcity and drought. Students can contribute by adopting water-saving habits, such as turning off faucets when not in use, fixing leaks, and using water-efficient appliances. Additionally, promoting the use of water-saving technologies in agriculture, like drip irrigation, can significantly reduce water consumption.

Furthermore, implementing policies to protect and restore ecosystems, such as wetland and forest conservation, can help maintain water availability. Communities can also develop water-sharing agreements and invest in water infrastructure to ensure equitable distribution of water resources.

In conclusion, water scarcity and drought are pressing issues that demand our attention as students concerned about the environment. By understanding the causes and impacts of these conditions, as well as implementing sustainable water management practices, we can work towards a more environmentally resilient future. Let us strive to conserve water, protect ecosystems, and promote sustainable solutions to ensure the availability of this precious resource for generations to come.

Addressing Water Pollution and Contamination

Water is a precious resource that is essential for all life on Earth. However, due to human activities and negligence, our water sources are becoming increasingly polluted and contaminated. This subchapter aims to educate students on the importance of addressing water pollution and contamination and provide practical solutions for a sustainable future.

Water pollution occurs when harmful substances enter water bodies, making them unfit for consumption or supporting aquatic life. Industrial waste, agricultural runoff, and improper waste disposal are some of the major contributors to water pollution. Contamination, on the other hand, refers to the presence of disease-causing organisms or toxic substances in water sources. It poses a significant threat to public health and the environment.

As students, it is crucial to understand the consequences of water pollution and contamination. Not only does it harm aquatic ecosystems and biodiversity, but it also affects human health. Consuming contaminated water can lead to various waterborne diseases, causing illness and even death. Additionally, polluted water negatively impacts agriculture, as crops and livestock rely on clean water for growth.

To address water pollution and contamination, we must first raise awareness and promote responsible water management practices. Students can play an active role in conserving water by adopting simple yet effective measures such as turning off taps when not in use, fixing leaky faucets, and using water-efficient appliances. Additionally, advocating for stricter regulations on industrial waste disposal and agricultural practices can significantly reduce pollution.

Furthermore, implementing proper wastewater treatment systems is crucial in ensuring that water is safely returned to the environment. Students can learn about different treatment methods and encourage their communities to invest in sustainable wastewater management infrastructure.

Another essential aspect of addressing water pollution is preventing contamination. This can be achieved by promoting proper waste disposal practices, encouraging regular testing of water sources, and implementing water purification techniques when necessary. Students can engage in community initiatives to raise funds for water purification systems or organize educational campaigns on the importance of clean drinking water.

In conclusion, addressing water pollution and contamination is essential for the sustainability of our environment and the well-being of all living beings. As students, we have the power to make a difference by adopting responsible water management practices, advocating for stricter regulations, and promoting awareness in our communities. Let us join hands in preserving our water resources for future generations to come. Together, we can create a world where clean and safe water is accessible to all.

Balancing Water Needs with Environmental Concerns

In today's world, the importance of water management cannot be overstated. As students, you have the power to make a positive impact on the environment by understanding the delicate balance between water needs and environmental concerns. In this subchapter, we will explore various strategies and practices that can help us achieve sustainable water management practices while minimizing harm to our environment.

One of the key principles of balancing water needs with environmental concerns is the concept of water conservation. By conserving water, we can reduce the strain on our water resources and ensure their availability for future generations. Simple actions, such as turning off the tap while brushing your teeth, taking shorter showers, or fixing leaky faucets, can go a long way in conserving water. Additionally, implementing water-efficient technologies in our homes, schools, and communities can significantly reduce water consumption without compromising our daily needs.

Another crucial aspect of sustainable water management is the protection of natural ecosystems. Many plants and animals rely on specific water conditions to survive and thrive. By understanding and respecting these ecological needs, we can ensure that our water usage does not harm or disrupt these delicate systems. For example, avoiding excessive water extraction from rivers and lakes can maintain water levels necessary for the survival of aquatic life.

Furthermore, we must address the issue of water pollution. Industrial activities, agriculture, and improper waste disposal practices can all contribute to water pollution, degrading the quality and availability of this precious resource. As students interested in environmental sustainability, it is essential to advocate for responsible waste management and support initiatives that promote the use of eco-friendly alternatives and practices.

Lastly, raising awareness about the importance of balancing water needs with environmental concerns is crucial. By educating ourselves and others about the impact of our actions on water resources and ecosystems, we can inspire positive change. Encourage your peers and community to adopt sustainable water management practices, participate in local clean-up events, or engage in initiatives that promote water conservation and protection.

In conclusion, as students passionate about the environment, we have a responsibility to balance our water needs with environmental concerns. By practicing water conservation, protecting natural ecosystems, preventing water pollution, and raising awareness, we can contribute to sustainable water management practices. Remember, even small actions can make a significant difference. Let's work together to ensure a future where water resources are preserved for generations to come.

Chapter 9: The Future of Water Management and Student Sustainability

Exploring Emerging Technologies and Innovations

In today's rapidly advancing world, the impact of emerging technologies and innovations on environmental sustainability cannot be overlooked. As students passionate about the environment, it is crucial for us to be aware of the latest developments that can help us address the pressing water management challenges we face. This subchapter, "Exploring Emerging Technologies and Innovations," delves into some of the most promising solutions that can revolutionize water management practices and drive us towards a more sustainable future.

One such innovation is the Internet of Things (IoT), which involves connecting everyday objects to the internet to collect and exchange data. IoT can be utilized to create smart irrigation systems that monitor soil moisture levels, weather forecasts, and plant water needs. By optimizing water usage based on real-time data, these systems help conserve water and prevent over-irrigation, reducing both water waste and energy consumption.

Another emerging technology that holds great potential is artificial intelligence (AI). AI can be employed in water management to analyze vast amounts of data and make accurate predictions about water availability, quality, and usage patterns. This enables better decision-making, resource allocation, and early detection of water-related issues such as leaks or contamination, allowing for timely intervention and minimizing environmental impact.

Furthermore, desalination technologies are gaining momentum as a solution to freshwater scarcity. Desalination involves removing salt and other impurities from seawater or brackish water to make it suitable for drinking and irrigation. While traditional desalination methods are energy-intensive, new breakthroughs such as membrane distillation and solar-powered desalination offer more sustainable alternatives, making desalination a viable option for regions facing water scarcity.

Additionally, advances in nanotechnology and biotechnology are opening up exciting possibilities in water treatment and purification. Nanomaterials can remove pollutants at the molecular level, while biotechnology offers eco-friendly solutions by harnessing the power of microorganisms to clean contaminated water. These cutting-edge technologies have the potential to provide access to safe and clean water for communities around the world.

By familiarizing ourselves with these emerging technologies and innovations, we can contribute to the ongoing efforts in environmental sustainability. As students, we have the power to drive change and shape the future of water management practices. Let us embrace these advancements, explore their potentials, and work towards a water-conscious world where every drip counts in saving our precious crops and ensuring a sustainable future for generations to come.

Student-Led Initiatives and Projects for Water Conservation

Water is a vital resource that sustains life on our planet. With growing concerns about water scarcity and environmental degradation, it is crucial for students to take an active role in conserving and managing this precious resource. Student-led initiatives and projects for water conservation can play a significant role in promoting sustainability and creating a positive impact on the environment.

One effective way for students to contribute to water conservation is by raising awareness among their peers and the wider community. By organizing educational campaigns, workshops, and events, students can highlight the importance of water conservation and the potential consequences of its mismanagement. These initiatives can inspire others to adopt water-saving practices and make conscious choices in their daily lives.

Another impactful way to conserve water is by implementing practical projects within the school grounds. Students can collaborate with teachers, administrators, and local organizations to design and install water-efficient systems, such as rainwater harvesting, drip irrigation, and water recycling. These projects not only conserve water but also serve as living examples for others to replicate in their own homes and communities.

Furthermore, students can initiate community outreach programs, partnering with local authorities and organizations to address water-related issues in their neighborhoods. For instance, they can organize clean-up drives along rivers and lakes, conduct water quality testing, or engage in tree planting activities to protect local water sources. By involving the community, students can create a collective effort towards sustainable water management.

In addition to these initiatives, students can also utilize technology to promote water conservation. Developing mobile applications, websites, or social media campaigns can help disseminate information, provide tips on water-saving practices, and encourage behavioral changes. By leveraging technology, students can reach a wider audience and inspire global action towards water conservation.

To conclude, student-led initiatives and projects for water conservation are essential in addressing the current environmental challenges we face. By raising awareness, implementing practical projects, collaborating with the community, and utilizing technology, students can drive positive change in water management. By taking action today, students can create a sustainable future where water resources are preserved for generations to come. Let us join hands and make a difference in the conservation of our most precious resource – water.

Advocating for Sustainable Water Policies and Practices

Water is a precious resource that is vital for all life on Earth. Yet, in recent years, we have witnessed the alarming depletion and pollution of our water sources due to unsustainable practices. As students, we have the power to make a difference by advocating for sustainable water policies and practices, and ensuring a better future for our environment.

One of the first steps in advocating for sustainable water policies is to understand the current state of water resources. By researching and gathering information about our local water sources, we can identify any issues and areas that need improvement. This information will serve as a foundation for our advocacy efforts.

Once we have a clear understanding of the challenges, it is important to raise awareness among our peers and the wider community. We can organize awareness campaigns, workshops, and events to educate others about the importance of conserving water and the negative impacts of unsustainable practices. Through these initiatives, we can encourage others to adopt water-saving habits in their daily lives.

Advocacy also involves engaging with local authorities and policymakers. By reaching out to them, we can express our concerns and demand the implementation of sustainable water policies. It is crucial to present well-researched arguments and provide feasible solutions that address the specific environmental issues in our region. Our voices, combined with scientific evidence, can have a meaningful impact on decision-making processes.

Additionally, we can support organizations and initiatives that are already working towards sustainable water management. By volunteering, fundraising, or participating in their activities, we can contribute to their efforts and amplify their message. Collaborating with like-minded individuals and groups will strengthen our advocacy and create a larger impact.

Furthermore, as students, we have the opportunity to influence our educational institutions to prioritize sustainable water practices. We can propose projects, workshops, or research programs that promote water conservation and management. By integrating these topics into our curriculum, we can ensure that future generations are well-informed and equipped to tackle water-related challenges.

Advocating for sustainable water policies and practices is not just about securing a better future for our environment; it is also about safeguarding our own well-being. By working towards a sustainable water future, we can ensure that we have access to clean and safe water for generations to come. Let us join forces, raise our voices, and advocate for a world where water is conserved and protected, for the benefit of our planet and all its inhabitants.

Chapter 10: Conclusion and Call to Action

Reflecting on the Importance of Water Management

Water is an essential resource for all living beings on Earth. From quenching our thirst to ensuring crops grow, water plays a vital role in sustaining life. However, with the increasing global population and climate change, the availability of clean and fresh water is becoming a growing concern. In this subchapter, we will delve into the significance of water management and why it is crucial for students to understand and actively participate in sustainable practices.

Water management refers to the process of planning, developing, distributing, and utilizing water resources efficiently and sustainably. It involves understanding the water cycle, implementing conservation measures, and adopting innovative technologies to ensure the availability of water for present and future generations.

One of the main reasons why water management is critical is its direct impact on the environment. Inefficient use of water can lead to the depletion of freshwater sources, the degradation of ecosystems, and the loss of biodiversity. By managing water resources responsibly, students can help mitigate these negative effects and contribute to preserving our planet's delicate balance.

Furthermore, water management is closely linked to the sustainability of agriculture. Agriculture is the largest consumer of freshwater globally, accounting for around 70% of all water withdrawals. Students interested in the environment and agricultural practices should understand the importance of optimizing water use in farming to ensure food security while minimizing water waste. Efficient irrigation systems, crop selection, and soil conservation techniques are all crucial aspects of sustainable water management in agriculture.

Water management also intersects with other environmental issues, such as climate change and pollution. Rising temperatures and changing precipitation patterns are altering the availability and quality of water, making it even more essential to manage this resource wisely. Additionally, pollution from industrial and domestic sources threatens the integrity of water bodies, making proper management and treatment crucial for maintaining water quality and safeguarding human health.

By reflecting on the importance of water management, students can gain a deeper understanding of the role they play in shaping a sustainable future. They can explore ways to reduce their water footprint, advocate for responsible water policies, and engage in community initiatives that promote water conservation and protection.

In conclusion, water management is a critical aspect of environmental sustainability. Students have a unique opportunity to learn about the importance of water management and actively contribute to preserving this precious resource. By reflecting on the significance of water management, students can become informed and empowered advocates for a water-secure and environmentally-conscious future.

Empowering Students to Make a Difference

In today's world, the need to protect and preserve our environment has never been more crucial. As students, you have the power to make a significant impact on the world around you. By understanding the importance of water management and sustainability, you can become agents of change and contribute to the betterment of our planet.

Water is the essence of life, and it plays a vital role in sustaining ecosystems, agriculture, and human life. However, with the growing population and increasing demands, our water resources are facing numerous challenges. From droughts to pollution, the need for effective water management practices has become more apparent than ever before.

This subchapter aims to empower you, as students, to take charge and make a difference in the field of environmental sustainability. By incorporating water management practices into your daily lives, you can help conserve this precious resource and ensure its availability for future generations.

One way to make a difference is by practicing water conservation in your everyday routines. Simple actions such as turning off the tap while brushing your teeth, taking shorter showers, and fixing leaky faucets can significantly reduce water wastage. By being mindful of your water usage, you can contribute to preserving this valuable resource.

Another way to empower yourself is by spreading awareness about water management and sustainability. Use your voice to educate and inspire others about the importance of conserving water. Organize awareness campaigns, create informative posters, or deliver presentations in your school or community to encourage others to join the cause.

Furthermore, you can actively participate in community initiatives related to water management. Join local organizations or volunteer for projects that focus on water conservation, river clean-ups, or planting trees near water bodies. By getting involved, you can contribute directly to improving the environment and creating a positive impact in your community.

Lastly, don't underestimate the power of education. Seek opportunities to learn more about water management, sustainable practices, and environmental science. By acquiring knowledge and understanding the challenges and solutions related to water conservation, you become better equipped to make informed decisions and influence others positively.

Remember, every drop counts, and your actions can create a ripple effect that will benefit our environment. By empowering yourself as a student, you have the potential to become a catalyst for change and contribute to building a sustainable future. Together, let's make a difference and ensure a healthier planet for generations to come.

Taking Steps Towards a Sustainable Future

In this subchapter, we will delve into the crucial topic of taking steps towards a sustainable future, focusing specifically on the environment. As students, you hold the power to create a positive impact on our planet, and understanding the importance of sustainable practices is the first step towards achieving this goal.

Sustainability, at its core, revolves around meeting the needs of the present without compromising the ability of future generations to meet their own needs. In the context of the environment, it means making conscious choices that minimize harm to our planet and promote its long-term health.

One key area where your actions can make a significant difference is water management. As we have discussed throughout this book, water is a precious resource that is essential for all life on Earth. By adopting sustainable practices in water management, you can contribute to a healthier environment.

Firstly, conserving water is of utmost importance. Simple actions like turning off the tap while brushing your teeth, taking shorter showers, and fixing leaky faucets can save gallons of water every day. Additionally, using low-flow fixtures and appliances can significantly reduce water consumption without compromising your daily needs.

Another vital aspect of sustainable water management is responsible irrigation. By using efficient watering methods, such as drip irrigation or rainwater harvesting, you can minimize water wastage while ensuring plants receive the necessary moisture. Additionally, choosing drought-resistant plants for your gardens can reduce the need for excessive watering.

Moreover, it is essential to be mindful of pollution prevention. Chemicals and pollutants that enter our water bodies can have detrimental effects on aquatic ecosystems and human health. By choosing eco-friendly products, properly disposing of hazardous materials, and avoiding excessive use of fertilizers and pesticides, you can help protect our water resources and the environment as a whole.

Furthermore, spreading awareness and advocating for sustainable practices are crucial steps towards a sustainable future. Encouraging your peers, educators, and local communities to adopt environmentally friendly habits can create a ripple effect and contribute to a wider movement for change.

In conclusion, taking steps towards a sustainable future is a responsibility that falls upon each and every one of us, including students like yourselves. By understanding the importance of sustainable practices, conserving water, implementing responsible irrigation, preventing pollution, and spreading awareness, you can play a significant role in safeguarding the environment for future generations. Remember, the choices you make today will shape the world you inherit tomorrow.

Milton Keynes UK
Ingram Content Group UK Ltd.
UKHW020252221123
432980UK00017B/1241